Imagine a Puffin

Stanford Apseloff

OHIO DISTINCTIVE PUBLISHING

Columbus, Ohio

For my son, Evan, and his beautiful mother, Sveta.

Text and photographs by Stanford Apseloff. No puffins were touched or disturbed for any of the photographs.

To inquire about special discounts for bulk purchases, please contact Ohio Distinctive Publishing by email: books@ohio-distinctive.com or by phone: 614-459-3100.

10 9 8 7 6 5 4 3 2 1
102012-1-5000-JO-37040

Printed in the United States of America.

ISBN 978-1-936772-05-6

Library of Congress Control Number: 2012917782

Ohio Distinctive Publishing · 6500 Fiesta Drive · Columbus OH 43235
www.ohio-distinctive.com

Imagine a bird like a penguin that flies.
Imagine bright colors for beak, feet, and eyes.

Imagine webbed feet that make swimming a breeze
On waters so frigid the waves nearly freeze.

Imagine an island with cliffs but no trees—
Dainty white flowers, a salty sea breeze.

Picture it now, way up north far away—
Where waves shower shores with a fine ocean spray.

Let's go to that island—let's do it right now.
Imagine with me, and I'll show you how!

And what might our island adventure reveal?
Something amazing—*those birds are real.*

Puffins they're called, and they're ten inches tall
With a beak that's as bright as a red circus ball.

So now it's decided—you'll come with me!
The adventure begins! It starts out at sea....

A flash from the lighthouse and cold ocean spray
Greet captain and crew on a blustery day.

Machias Seal Island, I see you at last!
Are landing boats ready?—we'll drop anchor fast.

Let's scamper ashore where the rocks let us pass,
Then climb to high ground crowned with flowers and grass,

Where thousands of puffins parade in fine style
With feathered tuxedo and tri-colored smile.

That shed to the right is where birdwatchers hide.
The puffins can't see any people inside.

A shed to watch birds is a birdwatcher's "blind,"
And as you can see, the puffins don't mind.

Let's venture inside, and we'll watch them from there.
You'll hear flopping feet and see birds everywhere.

Look! Here are two not a stone's throw away,
A typical pair— one's looking this way.

These two look alike from their heads to their tails,
But lady birds often are smaller than males.

Do all look alike? To you and me, maybe.
But certainly not to a lone puffin baby.

Perhaps when *they* look at people who visit,
The puffins all ask, "Which one of them is it?"

Imagine island living with spectacular views.
Wings make it easy to go where you choose.

Flying about would help you stay fit,
And you'd get where you're going, lickety split!

The puffin's stout wings are short for its size,
Just two feet across—a wonder it flies.

Imagine strong wings, propelling you high,
Feather tips blurring against sea and sky.

Would you trade arms for a pair of such wings?
The least that you'd miss is a place for your rings.

But imagine the freedom to fly anytime,
To go anywhere, and land on a dime,

With wind in your face, the sun to the south,
And freshly caught fish in your highly skilled mouth!

Puffins fly in great circles not far from their nests
To ward off the seagulls and other such pests.

Some head out to sea where they eat every day.
Often they'll fly many miles away.

Imagine you're adrift, awaiting evening stars,
Far from building lights or the sound of passing cars.

From autumn through spring, puffins live on the ocean,
Not bothered at all by the sea's rocking motion.

They dive deep for fish, and they float in their sleep—
and do it quite soundly without counting sheep.

At the end of spring, as their instincts command,
The puffins will always return to the land.

It's time for puffin nesting, and the ocean's cold water
Is no place to hatch a son or a daughter.

A puffin pair lays only one egg per year.
That's not many offspring for parents to rear.

But millions inhabit the ocean's north waters
All thanks to each one of those lone sons and daughters.

Some live farther north than the great Arctic Circle
In weather so cold it would make you turn purple.

Imagine a home with no roof overhead,
With narrow rock walls, maybe grass for a bed.

Or a home that's no more than a hole in the ground,
Lined with soft objects the puffin has found.

These birds have no need for a nest made of sticks—
Boulders and burrows protect eggs and chicks.

The babies stay hidden until they can fly,
A week or two after the end of July.

I'd show you one now, but they really are hidden,
And walking near burrows is strictly forbidden!

Instead let's watch parents with fish in their beaks.
They feed baby chicks for about seven weeks.

Parent puffins fish for herring, shrimp, and eel.
Sometimes all at once—try *that* with rod and reel.

The trick is that their mouths have many tiny spines
That do a better job than fancy hooks and lines.

The babies wait in burrows to get their favorite dish.
It could be shrimp or squid, but chances are it's fish.

Bobbing for apples isn't easy to do.
Bobbing for fish—that's difficult too!

Puffins make it look easy—they catch quite a few—
Enough in one mouthful to make a fine stew.

Fishermen tell tales of the one that got away,
But this proud puffin lands the largest of the day.

She goes back to her burrow, walking and hopping,
Up and down rocks, occasionally stopping.

Behavior and antics are fun to observe.
I frequently wonder what purpose they serve.

Fun and games, maybe, or is there more to it?
They're active right now—let's watch while they do it.

Some puffins, like this one, are never impressed.
The one in the back is doing his best.

It's not fencing with foils, but the principles apply.
Seek high ground. Don't get poked in the eye.

Dropping in for a visit? For puffins, why not?
It's socially proper—they do it a lot.

When you have wings, even falling is fun.
When you can fly, there is no need to run.

Puffins and razorbills never rub shoulders,
But sometimes you'll see that they share the same boulders.

No arms for a hug—no lips for a kiss.
Puffin affection looks mostly like this.

Though I never can tell what a puffin is thinking,
I do know what puffins like eating and drinking.

No it's not biscuits and jam with their tea—
It's various fish, and they drink from the sea.

Let's have some fun with the puffins we're viewing.
Imagine they're human—so what are they doing?

They're pondering last night's good news—I can tell.
The markets are up and the weather is swell.

This master magician will make you believe
Fantastical things with the tricks up his sleeve.

Make way, rubber ducks—come look, girls and boys—
Here's the new top model for upscale bath toys!

Important news for all those involved—
The case of the missing feather is solved!

Daredevil or clown?—you be the judge.
He could lose his balance with just a small nudge.

Here's a bold fellow with something to say.
Or could it be, "Get out of my way!"?

Grooms for a wedding never looked so fine.
With no clothes on they're dressed to the nines!

They're perfectly posed for the formal occasion—
No need for a top hat or fancy carnation.

No time for coffee—no time for a chat.
He's off with no newspaper, jacket, or hat.

Naughty youngsters drop pennies from ultra-high places.
When the parents find out—oh, the look on their faces!

They jockey for position at the start of a race.
No one wants to finish in just second place!

The candidates debate before an undecided crowd.
The rules do clearly state no interrupting is allowed.

Seriously though, puffins talk up quite a storm,
Especially on land, where talking is the norm.

They sound a bit like chainsaws—an unexpected noise—
From birds that look an awful lot like little children's toys.

You'd think they'd have a key to wind them up to walk,
And possibly to flap their wings and maybe even talk.

But puffins aren't for play; they're very special birds,
Singularly beautiful beyond my skill with words.

And on that note, our captain calls!—our puffin journey ends.
But come back anytime you like to see our puffin friends.

The way is always easy, and the weather's always fair.
You need no boat or compass and no special clothes to wear.

This one small book can do the trick, almost anywhere—

Just turn the pages one by one. Imagine you are there.